THE FLYING DUTCHMAN

Richard Wagner

The Flying Dutchman

by RICHARD WAGNER

Pictures by

HELMUT LUCKMANN

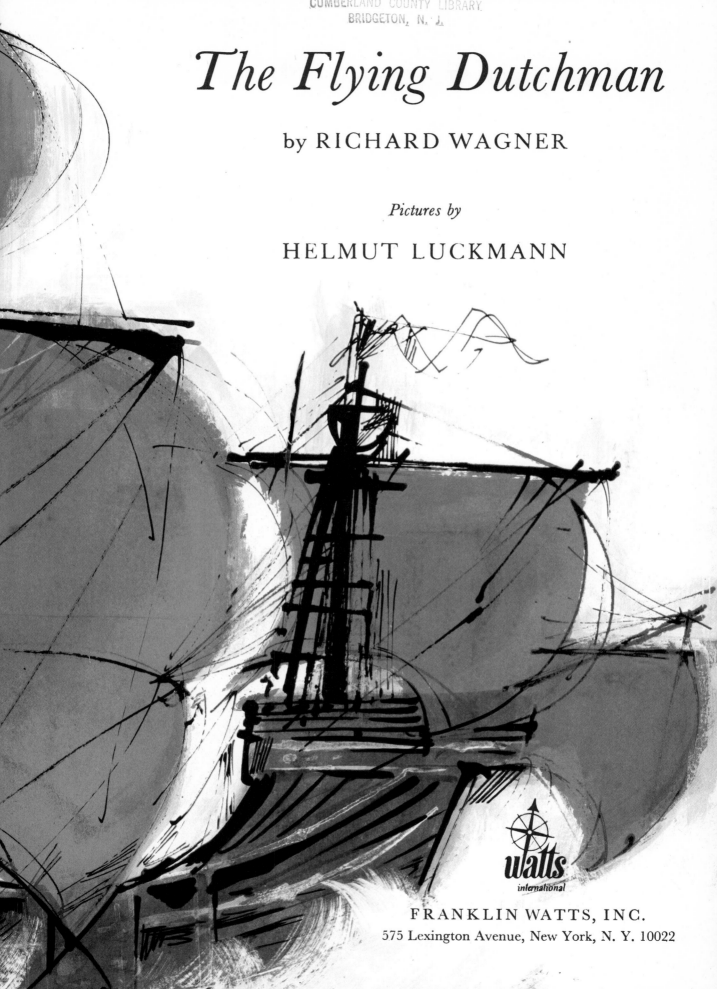

watts
international

FRANKLIN WATTS, INC.
575 Lexington Avenue, New York, N. Y. 10022

This edition first published in the United States of America by
Franklin Watts Inc. and in Great Britain by
J. M. Dent & Sons Ltd., 1969. All rights reserved.
Illustrations © 1969 Carl Ueberreuter Druck und Verlag (M. Salzer), Wien
English Text © 1969 J. M. Dent & Sons Ltd. and Franklin Watts Inc.
Designed and produced by Carl Ueberreuter Verlag, Vienna
Printed in Austria
Library of Congress Catalog Card number 69-11378

WAGNER AND *THE FLYING DUTCHMAN*

The fate of Europe was decided in and around Leipzig in the days between the 16th and 19th October, 1813, when Napoleon was defeated at the Battle of the Nations. While the cannons thundered outside the city, a five-month-old baby lay in his cradle. Richard was the seventh son of Friedrich Wagner, an actuary, who was also a theatre enthusiast and an ardent student of literature. When Richard was only a few months old his father died of typhus, the dread disease which the soldiery had brought into the city.

Richard's mother, Rosina, a miller's daughter, later married the actor Ludwig Geyer, who cared devotedly for the large family. Richard was brought up to believe he was his own father. Ludwig Geyer wanted Richard to be a painter; he, too, died too soon to see where the boy's real talent lay. But when Richard was only seven years old he cheered his stepfather, who was then on his deathbed, by playing on the piano extracts from Karl Maria von Weber's recent opera, *Der Freischütz*.

When he was eleven Richard wrote a bloodthirsty tragedy in which fortytwo people died in five acts. He had to make most of the departed spirits re-appear or he would have run short of characters in the last act.

At concerts given at the Gewandhaus in Leipzig Richard Wagner heard for the first time the music of Beethoven, which made a deep impression on him. The overture to *Egmont* inspired him so much that he determined to become a musician. At about this time Wagner saw in Leipzig the great actress and singer Wilhelmine Schröder-Devrient. He was so thrilled by her performance, he rushed over to his friend's lodgings, snatched a sheet of paper and hastily wrote her an impassioned letter. In it he declared that his life had only now assumed meaning. He begged her to remember that, should she one day hear his name acclaimed in the world of art, it was she who had inspired him to be great.

Ten years later Richard Wagner, now a conductor in Riga, was forced to flee from his debts. A good friend had robbed him "in the most perfidious manner" of his position with the opera company. Without a passport he made his way by the most adventurous and dangerous route across the Russian border and on to Paris. In his pocket he carried two completed acts of his third opera, *Rienzi*. While crossing the Baltic on the way from Pillau to London, the sailing vessel *Thetis* ran into serious trouble. The captain took shelter from the raging storm in a Norwegian fjord. There, in a flash, Wagner had a vision of *The Flying Dutchman*. He had already read the story by Heinrich Heine. Now he heard it again in the tales of the sailors.

In Paris the vision assumed artistic form. Starving, pursued by his creditors, "in darkness and destitution", as he himself wrote on the title page of the work, Wagner composed *The Flying Dutchman* in a fever of creative effort. The libretto was completed within ten days, the music within seven weeks. It was the first step away from the conventional opera and towards the musical drama, which he recreated in his subsequent works from *Tannhäuser* to *Parsifal*. The first performance of *The Flying Dutchman* took place on 2nd January 1843, at the Court Theatre in Dresden. Senta, the female lead, was played by—Wilhelmine Schröder-Devrient.

Alexander Witeschnik

Throughout the world, on every coast, sailors tell of a ghost ship, a strange apparition of black masts and blood-red sails, which they sometimes glimpse through stormclouds, fleeing across the ocean like a thing accursed.

The name of this ship is *The Flying Dutchman*.

Long years ago, so the legend tells, a ship rounding Cape Horn was overtaken by a terrible tempest which raged for many days. With satanic fury the icy wind lashed the sea into mountainous waves. In the lowering darkness sky and sea were one, wave upon wave swept over the deck of *The Flying Dutchman*, the hardiest seamen, young and old, all gave up hope.

All save the Captain. He defied the raging elements. Fair weather or foul, he was determined to round the Cape and no terror would stop him. The tempest might double its force, the ship be driven towards the threatening rocks—but the Captain, grim und proud, fought the wild power of the storm.

"In all eternity I will not give up!" he cried with boastful arrogance. His oaths and wild curses were drowned by the roar of the gale and the surging sea. But there was one who heard his oath and took the Dutchman at his word—the Devil.

The Devil's voice spoke in the wind. "In all eternity?" he mocked.

"I shall round the Horn though the Devil be my pilot!" shouted the Captain. "I shall never give up. Never!"

Then the wind flung back the Devil's curse: "So be it! You shall round the Horn but never more set foot on land. From this day forward, as long as ships sail the seas, as long as the tides ebb and flow, you shall sail on to all eternity!"

And so *The Flying Dutchman*, her Captain and her crew, came through the storm, escaped the rocks. But now the Dutchman understood the bargain he had made. He could not bring his ship to shore. They were all doomed to roam the seas for ever. They could not even hope for death.

Then Heaven sent an angel to the Captain, the Dutchman, to give hope in his despair. The angel told him that if he could find a girl who would be faithful to him unto death, he would be saved. But that only once in every seven years of crossing the seas would the Dutchman be allowed to go ashore in search of a girl whose love would be unchanging and bring him peace.

So, *The Flying Dutchman* haunted the seven seas—a ghost ship that neither time nor wind nor water could harm, as still as death. No gay singing ever resounded from her deck. Captain and crew seemed dead, and yet were not allowed to die.

Generations came and went. Nobody knew now how many times the span of seven years had passed but the legend is still

8

told. The Dutchman, men said, had each time had to put to sea again, for he never found a girl whose love released him from the curse.

The Norwegian ship *Solveig* was nearing her home port after a long voyage when she was overtaken by a violent storm and was obliged to run into a small bay for shelter. Here the captain, Daland, went ashore and climbed to the top of a cliff which rose above the bay. The storm was slowly moving away but in the grey distance waves were still rising high, rolling in mightily to surge against the rocky headlands.

In the clouded sky he could trace the dark outline of the mountains surrounding the shore, stretching to the north and south along the coast, cut by deep fjords and Daland recognized his own familiar country. Just beyond the mountains to the north lay his own village.

As Daland climbed down the cliff path to return to his ship he was thinking of his only child, Senta, the lovely fair-haired girl who was anxiously awaiting her father's return.

The sound of shouts and songs and laughter broke in upon his thoughts. The crew were in high spirits and Daland, always a strict captain, for once made no attempt to check them.

"Ahoy there, helmsman," he called, as he climbed aboard. "We are in the bay of Sandwike. I know it well. But for the storm, we should long since have been home."

For a while he stood watching the hustle and bustle on deck. Slowly, with night falling, the noise and merriment died down.

"Enough!" the captain called out to the crew. "Time for rest now; it's been a long day!"

Soon every soul aboard was below save Daland and the helmsman.

"You take the watch tonight," ordered the captain. "And no slackness, however quiet the night; you are on duty."

"Don't worry, Captain," replied the helmsman. "Sleep with an easy mind."

Daland went below to his cabin. The helmsman made his rounds, listening to the abating storm, watching the seagulls that circled the ship. Then, at last, he settled down in a wind-sheltered corner to keep watch.

No starlight broke through the clouds. Darkness and the dull, rhythmic rolling of the sea engulfed the lonely watchman.

He sat thinking of the girl who was waiting for him at home.

10

Helmsman: Through thun-der and storm from dis-tant seas, my dar-ling girl I come! O-ver tow-er-ing waves, with south-ern breeze, at last I'm sail-ing home! My dar-ling, were there no south wind, I nev-er could come to you. O fair south wind, to me be kind! My dar-ling, to me be true!

His song of tempests and thunder, of love and longing, rang out into the night.

Tomorrow's dawn was far off yet. The hours dragged on. Exhausted, the helmsman fell asleep.

He did not hear the strange sound of the wind rising, nor did he see the ship with blood-red sails and black masts appear on the horizon and fast approach the bay. Only once did he stir in his sleep, when *The Flying Dutchman* dropped anchor at the other side of the bay.

The time was up: after seven years at sea without respite, the ghost ship could seek a haven.

13

Dark shadows moved silently about the deck, but there was no sound of human voices.

A dark figure now detached itself from the ghostly crew—a pale, black-bearded man; slowly, he climbed down the ladder and made his way ashore. It was the Dutch Captain. For the first time in seven years he felt firm ground under his feet, and for a few hours he could seek the company of happy people. He had long given up hope of finding salvation among them. And yet, by a strange force, he was ever driven towards them.

The Dutchman looked across the water to where the *Solveig* lay.

Her captain and crew were fast asleep. What peace after a rough passage to come to a safe anchorage! Such was their lot, whilst he, who had long wished for nothing but death, was denied even a grave in the sea.

A man now appeared on the deck of the Norwegian ship. It was the captain himself, Daland. The sight of the strange ship startled him.

"Hey, helmsman!" Daland called. "Have you nothing to report?"

The helmsman rubbed the sleep out of his eyes.

"Nothing, Captain," he replied. "All is well on board."

The captain took the helmsman by the shoulder and shook him.

"Nothing, nothing at all?" he said angrily. "Do you call *this* keeping watch? Look there! Is it just my imagination? Do you see that ship? How long have you been asleep?"

At once the helmsman was wide awake.

No, this was not imagination! A stone's throw away, on the other side of the bay, lay a foreign ship. Nothing moved on deck. The sails were furled, the anchor cast, the crew asleep below. And he had heard and seen nothing.

For a moment the helmsman had an uncanny feeling something strange and sinister had happened. The ship over there with its black masts, blacker then the night-sky, had a deathly appearance. A chill ran down his spine.

Hastily the helmsman put the loud hailer to his lips.

"Ahoy there!" he called. There was no answer. The sound reverberating in the utter stillness seemed unreal. A faint echo resounded from the cliffs, but still no answer came. Nothing stirred on the foreign ship.

"They seem to be sleeping as heavily as we are."

But at this moment Daland noticed the lone dark figure standing on the shore.

"Never mind," he said. "I think I see the captain. Hey there,

sailor!" he called across to the shore. "Who are you and where do you come from?"

"Right across the world," replied the stranger. "Do you refuse me anchorage in this stormy weather?"

"God forbid, no!" answered Daland. "It's the custom of sailors to welcome strangers. But tell me, who are you?"

"I am Dutch."

Daland left his ship and came ashore.

The Dutchman made no move forward to meet him. A faint light, perhaps the shimmer of the moon upon the clouds, suddenly lighted his face.

What a ravaged face it was! What coldly glowing eyes! It reminded Daland of a picture he had at home of a legendary seaman.

"God be with you!" said Daland. "So you too have been driven to this rocky shore of ours? Has your ship suffered damage? My home port is near—"

"My ship is safe, it suffers no damage. But the gale has brought me to unfamiliar waters. I roam the seas from coast to coast in search of my homeland."

"How long have you been at sea?" asked Daland. Being near his own home he was touched by the fate of this homeless stranger.

"I cannot tell. Months, years... I have given up counting them," said the stranger, "it is a long time since I set foot on land and I am weary of searching. Will you not give me shelter in your home for a little while? You shall not regret your hospitality. My ship is laden with treasure."

Daland turned to glance at the Dutchman's ship—it was motionless and as quiet as a churchyard. His eyes showed compassion and curiosity. This man, with his pale face that showed no sign of emotion, was rich and yet, it seemed, could not enjoy his riches. Again the legend came to mind but legend was one thing, life another: this man was real.

18

"You are welcome to be my guest," said Daland. "In my home you shall be well looked after." And, not able to suppress his curiosity, he added: "But, may I ask, what cargo do you carry?"

At a sign from the Dutchman his ship came to life. Two sailors carried a chest ashore, put it in front of the two captains and in a moment were swallowed up again in the darkness of the ship.

The Dutchman opened the chest. It was filled to the brim with costly pearls and gold and precious stones.

Daland was speechless with amazement.

"This is only a small part of the treasures that I have on my ship," said the Dutchman. "But of what use is my wealth to me? I have neither wife nor child. All my treasures shall be yours if you make me welcome in your house." He paused for a moment. Then, looking out to sea, he asked: "Have you a daughter?"

"Yes. And she is a good child and my greatest happiness on earth."

"Let her be my wife." The Dutch captain's voice was eager and abrupt.

Daland was taken aback. Did the stranger believe that his riches could buy him happiness? And yet—as he looked into this face marked by suffering, he also saw before his mind's eye his daughter, Senta, as a happy bride, eager to accept the stranger's hand in marriage. He could not explain to himself why this picture came to him so clearly.

"Senta shall be yours, if you can win her love," he said finally. "She is beautiful and good. I wish with all my heart that you may like her." He was silent for a moment. Then he went on: "Senta has always been a faithful, obedient daughter. I am sure that she will heed her father's wish."

"A faithful daughter will also be a faithful wife."

Daland noticed the glimmer of hope in the Dutchman's eyes.

"You shall see her this very day," he said. "The wind is fair. In a few hours we shall be home."

"You sail ahead. My ship is fast and will catch up with yours," replied the Dutchman.

He watched Daland go aboard and was still standing on the shore when the Norwegian vessel, her anchor weighed, put to sea with spreading sail to the sound of the seamen's song.

The clouds had passed over, the waters were calm and in the east the new day dawned. Daland's ship glided out of the bay, leaving only a rippling wake behind her.

Chorus of girls

Hum and hum, good wheel, go whir _____ ring...

Ballad

Senta: Yo - ho - ho! Yo - ho - ho - ho! Yo - ho - ho! Yo____ ho! The ship was driv - en by the gale, blood red the can - vas, black the mast. On board the cap - tain, brave and pale...

When the *Solveig* had disappeared beyond the horizon the Dutchman boarded his own ship.

As the *Solveig* headed homewards, a fair wind filling her sails and the seamen's song ringing out to sea, the crew of *The Flying Dutchman* hoisted blood-red sails and silently steered the same course.

No-one in Daland's house was yet aware of the sailors' home-coming. That morning, as was their custom, the village girls had come to sit in the cosy spinning-room with Daland's daughter Senta and her old nurse Mary. They loved to hear the tales the old woman told of trolls and giants and magic spells, of fishermen and mermaids—and of that fleeing Dutch mariner, doomed by the Devil to wander the seas for ever: this was the legend old Mary told the girls this day. The hum of the spinning-wheels mingled with the chatter and laughter around the big fireplace.

Only Senta had no thoughts for her work, nor even for Erik, the young huntsman who loved her and would ask for her hand when her father came home. She was sitting apart from the others, idle, her spinning-wheel not turning, dreamily gazing at a picture on the wall of a storm-tossed ship with a pale, dark-bearded man at the helm. The fate of the Dutchman fired her imagination. She

was sure that if ever she met such a man she would know him by his burning, restless eyes. Deeper in despair than any other man, his need of love would be so much the greater.

"Senta, come and join us."

Senta paid no attention.

"She is not listening. She is dreaming again of her doomed sailor."

"What will Erik say? A huntsman is not to be trifled with."

The girls did not understand Senta. Mary had often told them the story of the Flying Dutchman and they felt only a vague pity as for someone long dead; their hearts were not moved by the cruel fate of that unhappy man.

Senta could bear the childish prattle of her friends no longer.

"Please, stop!" she cried. " That tale fills me with grief."

"Do not be angry," said Mary, soothingly. "Come spin—and forget about the Dutchman."

"How can I forget him? He is part of my life," burst out Senta. "How can he ever find salvation if there is no girl who thinks of him, no-one who is faithful to him? "

"Silly child," said Mary. "What good will it do if your heart bleeds with pity? You do not even know where this unhappy man is. Or if he really exists."

Mary and the girls were frightened by the wild look in Senta's burning eyes.

"I wish I could save him!" she cried. "*I* would be faithful to him unto death!"

"Senta!" the girls shouted, horrified.

But even when the door swung open and Erik burst into the room Senta did not seem to hear. Her eyes were fixed on the romantic picture on the wall as if it were alive.

"Your father is here!" said Erik. At these words Senta composed herself. She wanted to hurry out with the others to welcome her father, but Erik, catching her hand, stopped her.

"Senta, have you no word for me? " he asked her. "Stay a moment and tell me if I may hope . . ."

"Hope . . . for what? "

"You do not know? Has the evil spirit of the picture so bewitched you that you no longer love me? "

"Don't! I never said I loved you." Senta edged away, but Erik would not release her.

"Please, hear me," he begged. "I had a dream last night. I saw your father coming ashore with a strange sailor—I recognized the man in the picture. You rushed towards him—you did not see your father, your eyes were on the stranger."

"I threw myself at his feet . . . he lifted me up . . ." As in a dream Senta continued Erik's account.

"... and carried you off with him to sea like an eagle with a dove."

Enraptured, Senta whispered. "He is coming."

Erik had hoped that his dream might cure Senta of her obsession with this man of legend but instead he saw with horror that to her the Dutchman only seemed more real than ever. The young hunter stumbled out of the room.

Senta stood motionless, lost in her dream as the door opened and her father entered with the stranger.

28

The black-clad figure, the pale face framed by a dark beard, the eyes . . . Senta gazed at him; she had no greeting for her father, did not rush to meet him. She had eyes only for the stranger, who came slowly towards her.

"My child, are you not glad to see me?" asked Daland, amazed.

At last Senta collected herself and turned to greet her father. Then she said, "I am sorry, father, I was not attentive." In a hushed voice she added, "I am ready now," and immediately her gaze returned to the stranger.

"There now, this is much better," said Daland, smiling. "Bid the stranger welcome. He is a Dutchman and, like me, a sailor. We are good friends. And he is rich too," he added, with a laugh to

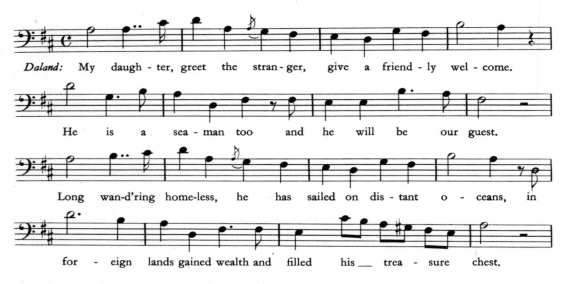

Daland: My daugh-ter, greet the stran-ger, give a friend-ly wel-come.

He is a sea-man too and he will be our guest.

Long wan-d'ring home-less, he has sailed on dis-tant o-ceans, in

for-eign lands gained wealth and filled his — trea-sure chest.

make light of his satisfaction. "I have told him much about you, so he is most impatient to meet you."

Turning to the stranger, he went on: " Tell me, did I praise her too much? Was it only a father's pride that made me speak as I did? "

There was no need to ask, for the Dutchman could not take his eyes off the beautiful girl. He was lost at the sight of her—with her slim figure, her golden hair and dreaming, blue eyes she stood like an angel before him.

Daland watched the scene with secret pleasure. He took from his pocket a beautiful pearl necklace and gave it to his daughter.

"Look at these priceless pearls," he said. "Would you not like them as a wedding present? They are but a few of the many treasures with which our guest's ship is laden . . . I will no longer keep it a secret, my child. I have brought you a suitor who is truly worthy of you. It would make me very happy if he were to win your love and take you for his wife."

Senta hardly glanced at the necklace in his hand. Steadily she gazed at the Dutchman.

Daland was puzzled at her strange conduct and at his guest's silence. He could think of nothing more to say; the two seemed to exist in a world of their own and had forgotten him.

"I had best leave you alone," he said. "Think of the happiness that might be yours, my child." And, turning to the Dutchman, he added: "Believe me, she is as true as she is beautiful."

With these words he left the room. Senta and the stranger were alone. It seemed to Senta that she had known and loved this pale, dark-eyed stranger, all her life.

In the quietness of the room time had no meaning for them.

And for the Dutch mariner, as he stood looking at Senta, the years of his damnation, of his ever-recurring despair passed like a

bad dream through his mind. Her beauty, her angelic purity filled his heart with new hope, but at the same time caused him to suffer tormenting doubts. What dreadful misfortune might he bring down upon this innocent girl if he linked his fate with hers? After the years of torment he could not believe that there might be a life of joy awaiting them; that this lovely girl, faithful till the end, would save his soul. Did she suspect the tragedy his life had been?

Senta did not suspect, she *knew,* had known it from the first moment the stranger had entered the house with her father. If the imagined man had moved her, how much more did the grief-stricken features of the living face touch her heart.

"I have voyaged far," said the Dutchman, "and stand before you a restless wanderer, a creature of grief and loneliness."

"Whoever you may be," replied Senta, "whatever evil fate pursues you, I will obey my father's wish."

"You do not ask what fate has brought me here? You are willing to give your word to a stranger? "

"My word and my hand. I will be faithful unto death."

Senta's eyes shone as she vowed to be true to the man whom she had met for the first time that day, who yet seemed no stranger to her. The Dutchman, after endless years of despair, dared to hope again.

As he took Senta's hand and drew her to him, he was roused by feelings that he had long since thought dead. Was it love that flowed through him like a warm stream or was it merely his desire for death and salvation? Was he trapping this innocent child for his own selfish ends? Was it asking too much of a young girl to bind herself to one who had made a pact with the Devil? If Senta should break her vow of unchanging love, she too would be damned, because she would have failed to rescue his soul. This girl, as no other before her, filled him with anguish and compassion.

Senta seemed to have guessed his thoughts, and her steadfast gaze dissolved all his doubts.

When Daland entered the room they did not even look up.

"I can see that you are of one mind," he said with satisfaction. "Senta, my child, are you willing to give this stranger your hand and heart in marriage? "

"Yes, Father. I will be faithful to him unto death."

Daland solemnly gave the Dutchman his hand and kissed his daughter. From the quayside came the sound of voices and laughter.

"Come with me—the people are already gathering outside to celebrate our return. Let us now announce your betrothal, and we shall have a double celebration."

From all the houses around the bay people had been coming out in great numbers to greet the returned captain and crew. The girls in their best finery laughed and jested with the sailors and the women, after so many lonely weeks, were happy to have their husbands safe home again.

The merrymaking went on till late in the evening. A clear night was setting in. The two ships lay close together in calm waters, their sails furled in safe haven at long last.

The *Solveig*, ablaze with lights, also echoed with laughter and merriment. The wine had put the sailors in a boisterous mood. No work today, no sleep, no lonely watch—neither for the captain nor for the helmsman. There was dancing, drinking and singing, and enough wine to quench the thirst of every sailor. No need to worry that supplies might run out, for all the while the girls brought more and more baskets laden with good things.

What a strange contrast the Dutchman's ship presented! No lights burned here, no sailor showed himself on deck. An eerie, unnatural silence hung over the ship, her black masts silhouetted against the moon-lit sky.

But Daland's sailors in their merriment paid no attention to the nearby ship. Let the foreign crew sleep, they thought—*they* had not come to anchor in their homeport; *they* could celebrate no reunion with anxious mothers, loving wives or faithful brides.

The girls, however, were curious about the foreign ship. How

Chorus of Norwegian sailors

Helms - man, leave ____ your watch! Helms - man, join ____ us here!

was it possible that all her crew lay fast asleep while the clear night was filled with song and laughter?

"What is the matter with the other ship?" they asked, calling up to Daland's crew. "No drinking, no singing, no light burning?"

"Let them sleep if they are tired!" the sailors told them, laughing. "They are probably old and grey and do not care for drink or merrymaking."

"But perhaps they have no wine?" suggested the girls defiantly. "You have had plenty and need no more. We shall soon see if they won't wake up when they smell wine and food." With these words they picked up their baskets and ran towards the silent ship.

"Go ahead," the helmsman called after them. "They'll never be able to resist *you*!" He filled his glass with wine, gave a toast, and drank it down at one draught. "To the tired crew alongside!"

But in vain the girls called — there was no answer from the foreign crew.

Daland's sailors whistled and shouted till they were hoarse. Their derisive cries grew wilder and wilder.

"Are you dead or are you ghosts? Yes, that's what it is, a ship of the dead—a ghost ship! Hahaha!"

But there came no answer, not a sound. There was no sign of any sailor.

This frightened the girls. Shuddering, they turned away from the ghost ship.

But the sailors would not give in and hurled more taunts and sneers at the foreign crew. They turned to the crowd. "Have you not heard of *The Flying Dutchman?* This is the very ship, right in front of your eyes! The gentlemen aboard have been dead for a few hundred years, so leave them in peace and come and join us. Let us dance and drink together. Why bother about them?"

The girls, however, were no longer in the mood for dancing. They handed their baskets to the sailors, glanced once more timidly at the Dutchman's ship and ran into Daland's house.

Louder and louder sang the sailors on Daland's ship, wildly stamping their feet to the rhythm of the music. "Helmsman, leave your watch, helmsman come and join us!" they sang. And the helmsman drank and sang with the rest of them.

Chorus of the crew of the Flying Dutchman

Broo-ding cap-tain, time to land, now that se-ven years have passed. Seek a faith-ful wo-man's hand! Faith-ful wo-man, love him well! Raise your hearts, hoy! Bride-groom, come, hoy! Winds be your bri-dal song . . .

Whether they had not noticed it in their excitement or it had happened suddenly no-one could say, but the sea around the Dutch vessel began to heave and a storm started to tear at her sails. A blue flame flared up on deck, bathing the ship in an eerie, spectral light. The Dutchman's crew now appeared, dark, ghost-like, singing the gruesome song of their captain and his damnation.

Oddly, though the sea might heave around the ghost ship, everywhere else it remained calm and smooth as before. And while a storm raged round the black masts, no breeze stirred on Daland's ship. Soon the sailors, terrified, were quiet and the singing and dancing on deck stopped abruptly.

But as suddenly as the sea and the storm had risen, as suddenly the waves became smooth again. And, as abruptly, a deadly silence returned to *The Flying Dutchman,* more sinister, more threatening than before.

And what meanwhile had happened in Daland's house?

Senta and her betrothed had insisted upon celebrating their betrothal quietly; and, reluctantly, Daland had agreed. For once

Senta had not been an obedient daughter, had not given in to her father's wish that their friends join in the celebrations.

Erik, full of fear and anxiety for Senta had left the house and sought the quietness of the woods to soothe his pain and still the turmoil of his thoughts. He did not return to the village till late in the evening, when he learned that the mysterious mariner was actually betrothed to Senta!

Despairingly he rushed to Daland's house to look for Senta. She had left the others, to be alone with her thoughts.

Senta turned deathly pale when he burst into the room. She ran away, out of the house, but Erik followed her.

"Senta! It is true . . .? "

Senta covered her face in distress. "Oh, do not ask me!" she implored him. "I must not see you, must not talk to you."

"It is true, then? " he asked again, his voice choking. Now he knew that his dream of the previous night had not deceived him. But he still refused to give Senta up easily.

"Have you forgotten all that was between us? You loved me and you were happy when I promised your father to protect you, before he set out on his last voyage. Do you not remember? We were standing on the cliff, hand in hand, and watched the ship till her sails disappeared beyond the horizon."

"Oh, stop, say no more! I must not listen to you!" cried Senta again.

"Who forbids you to speak to me? Who demands that you break your word? "

"My word? "

"Did you not promise to keep faith with me? "

"I made no promise."

"Do you deny it? Oh Senta, you surely cannot have forgotten!"

"Your memory is coloured by your hopes. Believe me, Erik, we were only children. I did not know what love for a man could really be . . . as I know now."

Erik, blinded by his love for her, could only say. "You promised to keep faith with me. Everyone knew we were betrothed."

Neither had noticed that the Dutchman had come out of the house and had overheard these words.

Erik's outburst made him stagger as if hit.

"You promised to keep faith with me." Erik repeated sadly.

The Dutchman stepped forward. In the cold light of the lantern his black figure cast a huge shadow. Utter despair was written in his bloodless, mask-like face, his flickering eyes.

"I am lost!"

Senta and Erik stood petrified.

"I am lost!" repeated the Dutchman. "Now you, too, have deceived me! Farewell! To sea forever!"

"No!"

Senta tore herself away from Erik's restraining grasp and with all her strength tried to hold the Dutchman back.

But he was already hurrying down to the shore. A shrill whistle woke the crew of his ship. "Hoist sail, weigh anchor!" he ordered.

Senta ran after him to the quayside. "Wait!" she cried at the top of her voice. "Do not doubt my love! I shall not break my word. I will keep my vow—to be faithful to you unto death!"

The Dutchman turned to look at her once more. "It is too late!" he said. "Be thankful to your guardian angel who saved you before it was too late. If you knew who I am—"

"I do! I know who you are, and I know of your fate," replied Senta. "I recognized you the moment I saw you."

"No, you do not really know who I am," answered the Dutchman. He pointed to his ship and its sails, whose reflection in the water made the sea glow blood-red. "Every sailor knows my name and trembles at the thought of encountering me. They call me the Flying Dutchman. I am damned, now and forever!"

He turned away and boarded his ship, without a further glance.

Senta stood as if paralysed. The ladder was pulled on board, the

ship drew away from the quay and soon *The Flying Dutchman* was sailing out of the bay.

Then suddenly Senta came to life. In a moment she had sprung on to the cliff path and was desperately scrambling up. She did not pause until she was on the edge of the dark cliff. From where she stood there was a deep drop to the sea.

The surging spray leapt up the cliff. A gust of wind caught her dress and loosened her hair.

46

Erik, numb with grief, was slow to move. But now an urgent fear possessed him.

"Help! Rescue her! She is lost!"

At his shrill cry Daland came rushing out of the house, followed by Mary and the girls.

Erik was too agitated to speak—but no words were needed to explain what was happening. From *The Flying Dutchman* with its blood-red sails there came drifting back to shore the sinister sound of the ghost crew singing—it was their song of perdition, a horrifying cry. "Yo-ho-ho."

Senta screamed.

"Senta, Senta! What are you doing? " cried Daland in deadly fear.

Senta paid no heed. Her lonely figure high up on the edge of the cliff was turned towards the disappearing ship. She did not hear her father's beseeching words or the imploring cries of Erik and her friends. She had forgotten that once she had been a happy child, a girl full of hope.

Senta held out her arms as if to make a last, desperate attempt to halt *The Flying Dutchman*. Then, in a clear voice, she cried:

"Praise be to the angel! Here I stand, faithful unto death!"

With these words Senta threw herself into the sea.

As the waves closed over her, the watchers on the shore saw *The Flying Dutchman* quietly sink into the water. The ghost ship left no trace behind. The waves became smooth over its grave. Captain and crew had found peace at last.

Senta, faithful unto death, had saved them.

But the legend of the Flying Dutchman lives on. When the waves dash against the shore and break upon the rocks, when the storm howls from the sea at night, waves and storm still tell the story of the ghost ship and its captain who in times long past roamed the seven seas.